Usborne
Sticker Book

# Nursery Rhymes

Illustrated by Rosalinde Bonnet

Designed by Laura Hammonds
Edited by Felicity Brooks

There are lots of stickers in the middle
of this book for you to stick on each page.

# Mary, Mary, Quite Contrary

Mary, Mary, quite contrary,
How does your garden grow?
With silver bells and cockle shells,
And pretty maids all in a row.

# Baa, Baa, Black Sheep

Baa, baa, black sheep,
Have you any wool?
Yes sir, yes sir,
Three bags full:

One for the master,
And one for the dame,
And one for the little boy
Who lives down the lane.

# Little Miss Muffet

Little Miss Muffet sat on a tuffet,

Eating her curds and whey;

Along came a spider,

Who sat down beside her,

And frightened Miss Muffet away.

# Jack and Jill

Jack and Jill went up the hill
To fetch a pail of water;
Jack fell down and broke his crown,
And Jill came tumbling after.

# Pat-a-cake,
# Pat-a-cake

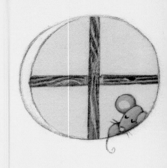

Pat-a-cake, pat-a-cake, baker's man,

Bake me a cake just as fast as you can.

Pat it and prick it, and mark it with B,

And put it in the oven for baby and me.

# See-Saw, Margery Daw

See-saw, Margery Daw,

Johnny shall have a new master;

He shall have but a penny a day,

Because he can't work any faster.

# Mary had a Little Lamb

Mary had a little lamb,

Its fleece was white as snow,

And everywhere that Mary went,

The lamb was sure to go.

Pat-a-cake,
Pat-a-cake

See-Saw,
Margery Daw

Mary, Mary,
Quite Contrary

Baa, Baa,
Black Sheep

# Little Bo-Peep

# Humpty Dumpty

# Hey Diddle, Diddle

Ride a Cock-horse

Twinkle, Twinkle, Little Star

Sing a Song
of Sixpence

Mary had a
Little Lamb

Hickory, Dickory,
Dock!

Little Miss Muffet

Jack and Jill

# Hickory, Dickory, Dock!

Hickory, dickory, dock!

The mouse ran up the clock;

The clock struck one,

The mouse ran down,

Hickory, dickory, dock!

# Little Bo-Peep

Little Bo-Peep has lost her sheep,
And doesn't know where to find them;
Leave them alone, and they'll come home,
Wagging their tails behind them.

# Sing a Song
of Sixpence

Sing a Song of Sixpence,

A pocket full

nd twenty

Baked in

When the pie wa

The birds began to sing,

Wasn't that a dainty dish

To set before the King?

# Humpty Dumpty

Humpty Dumpty sat on a wall,
Humpty Dumpty had a great fall;
All the King's horses and all the King's men
Couldn't put Humpty together again.

# Hey Diddle, Diddle

Hey diddle, diddle,

The cat and the fiddle,

The cow jumped over the moon;

The little dog laughed

To see such fun,

And the dish ran away with the spoon.

# Ride a Cock-horse

Ride a cock-horse to Banbury Cross,

To see a fine lady upon a white horse;

With rings on her fingers and bells on her toes,

She shall have music wherever she goes.

# Twinkle, Twinkle, Little Star

Twinkle, twinkle, little star,
How I wonder what you are,
Up above the world so high,
Like a diamond in the sky;
Twinkle, twinkle, little star,
How I wonder what you are.